Soppy Hoppy

A play by Jeanne Willis

Illustrated by Alexandra Colombo

Characters

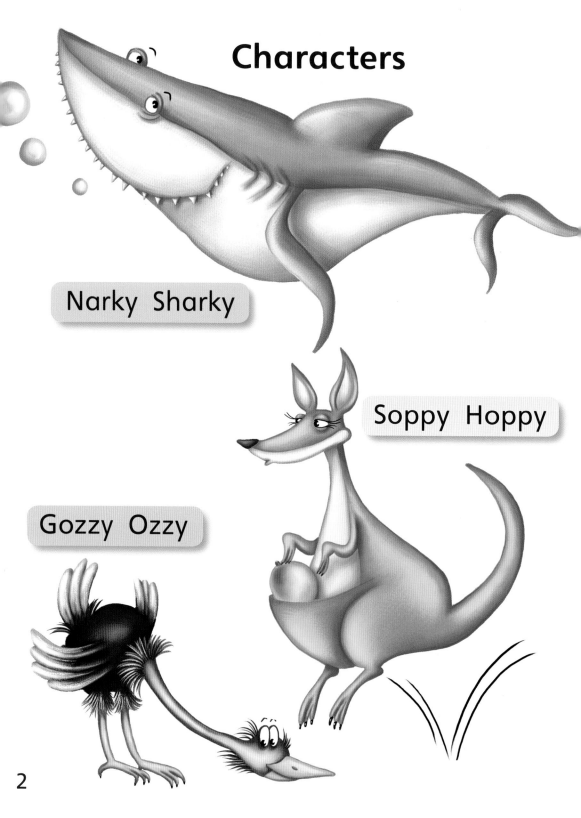

Narky Sharky

Soppy Hoppy

Gozzy Ozzy

Combat Wombat

Bossy Possum

Shocky Crocky

3

Narky Sharky: I am Narky Sharky. Let me tell my story, or I will eat you! One day, Soppy Hoppy was sleeping under a tree. CLONK! Something fell on her head.

4

Soppy Hoppy: Oh! The sun has fallen from the sky!

Narky Sharky: It was just a mango – but Soppy Hoppy did not know that.

Soppy Hoppy: I must go and tell the king that the sun has fallen.

Narky Sharky: On the way, she met Gozzy Ozzy.

Gozzy Ozzy: Where are you off to in such a hurry?

Soppy Hoppy: The sun has fallen. I must go and tell the king.

Gozzy Ozzy: I will come too.

6

Narky Sharky: On the way, they met Combat Wombat.

Combat Wombat: Where are you off to in such a hurry?

Soppy Hoppy: The sun has fallen. We must go and tell the king.

Combat Wombat: I will come too.

Narky Sharky: On the way, they met Bossy Possum.

Bossy Possum: Where are you off to in such a hurry?

Gozzy Ozzy: The sun has fallen. We are off to tell the king.

Bossy Possum: I will come too.

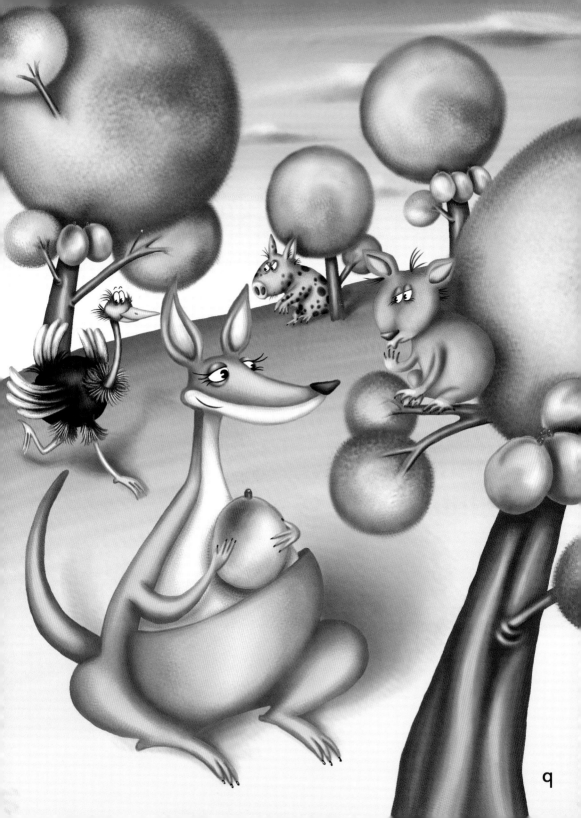

Narky Sharky: Soon, they came to a river.

Combat Wombat: Oh no! How can we get across?

Narky Sharky: Along came Shocky Crocky.

Shocky Crocky: Get on my back. I will take you across.

Narky Sharky: So they all sat on Shocky Crocky's back, and off he swam.

Shocky Crocky: Ha ha! Now I can eat you for dinner.

Soppy Hoppy: Oh no!

Gozzy Ozzy: Eek!

Combat Wombat: Help!

Bossy Possum: You rotter!

Narky Sharky: But along came Narky Sharky — that is me! What is all the fuss, Shocky Crocky?

Shocky Crocky: I just want to have my dinner.

Narky Sharky: So do I! Ha ha!

Shocky Crocky: Help! Shark!

Soppy Hoppy: Narky Sharky is eating Shocky Crocky!

Narky Sharky: Where was Shocky Crocky taking you?

Gozzy Ozzy: To see the king.

Combat Wombat: We need to tell him all about the sun falling down!

Soppy Hoppy: Yes, look – here is the sun!

Narky Sharky: That is not the sun – that is a mango!

Bossy Possum: Hooray! Will you take us back, Narky Sharky?

Narky Sharky: Thanks to me, they all got home. So you see, not all sharks are bad!